FANTASIA IN C MINOR (K. 39

ANALYTICAL NOTES

By AUBYN RAYMAR

THE title Fantasia applied to instrumental composition does not necessarily indicate anything as to the shape, content, or mood of a particular work. It implies neither form nor vagary.

The term was used even before that of Sonata for various early experiments in instrumental music when this began to assume independence of vocal composition. J. S. Bach adopted it for keyboard pieces of varying calibre and intent, separate movements, elaborate introductions to Fugues, or for the initial movement of a Suite; it was the original title even of his three-part Inventions.

Mozart's Fantasias, though few in number, also exemplify considerable divergence among themselves in point of design and content. They belong to the period, beginning in the year 1782, during which his modes of thought and expression were powerfully affected by the impact brought through his discovery of many works of J. S. Bach and Handel, and by study of Philip Emanuel Bach and other contemporary composers of Northern Germany.

The present Fantasia in C minor, composed between July 1782 and July 1784—a more precise date cannot be determined—exhibits more affinity to the manner of Philip Emanuel than of Sebastian Bach. Avoiding the contrapuntal style on the one hand, and, on the other, an indefiniteness of design like that of the Fantasia in D minor, Mozart unfolds, in strict Sonata form, a continuous melody accompanied by arpeggios and chords, and ranging with great variety of rhythmical feature through the entire compass of his keyboard.

It is mere conjecture that Mozart may have intended to make it, by adding others, the introductory movement of a more extended work. It is, at any rate, a movement at unity in itself, expressive of a single mood whose rather sombre passion, so far from seeking relief in the contrast of a lighter vein (at the formal opportunity of the second subject and the major key, for instance), appears rather to gather intensity with each new figure; until, in the Development, strictly confined to the main theme and passing through a series of modulations where the varied colour and the resonance of the whole keyboard are employed, the climax of passionate agitation is achieved with a prolonged repetition of the figure, in Iambic metre, of the meditative first phrase.

Bar 1.—The long arpeggio which sweeps upward to the initial note of melody is a characteristic recurrent figure of the main subject. A hurried effort to squeeze all its notes into the strict metronomic duration of the quaver beat would ill befit the gravity of the theme. Its first note, as the bass of a wide-spreading chord, should have appropriate emphasis, and the rest flow evenly to the summit. Similarly, without flurry, the unaccented scale of bar 4 (and bar 50) should slide as smoothly as possible on to the climactic note from which begins the slow re-descent of the melodic line. The chord implied on the 3rd and 4th beats, and through which the scale passes, is, of course, in bar 4 the first inversion of C minor and that of E flat major in bar 50.

3.—Beside attention to respective note-values in distinguishing the "voices," difference of tonal intensity should help to prevent their confusion: *e.g.*, to avoid the false melodic effect—

the lower voice should be rather lighter than the upper, and the syncopated crotchets D and G of the latter full-toned enough to carry the ear forward with certainty to the A♭ and F which respectively follow.

6.—Remembering the continuity of the melodic line, the ornamental shakes should not end abruptly staccato.

7.—From this point to the end of bar 13 some players would prefer to give both the lower parts to the left hand and reserve the right for the melody alone.

The thought here expressed becomes at bar 11 a little more tense in the quickened chromatic figure, and is repeated with still greater urgency at bar 13, where it provokes momentarily imitative response with very striking resultant dissonances which should not be softened. The descending bass should be clear throughout the passage.

17.—It is rarely that Mozart repeats in the major key (as in this case at bar 62) the second subject of a movement in the minor. Here this is a somewhat important element of relief, since the second theme proceeds in the rather brooding manner of the first. The disjunct progressions and the scales, however, now take a still wider range. Note the initial figure in bars 17, 18 and 19, and the long curve of bar 22, as well as the lesser ones of bars 23 and 24. Moreover, chords are thickened, scales in double notes and many shakes occur; while the chromatic phrase, though in reversed direction, is still present and provocative of imitation. (See bars 13-15 and 26, 27.)

The notes of the falling figure (bars 17, 18, 19) should be bold in tone and thus distinctly connected; the following staccato demisemiquavers lighter, very rhythmical, with a crescendo as they climb to the next peak.

The melodic character must be preserved through every bar of this section, and with especial care at bars 20-25 where an insensitive *bravura* method must not take the place of the tone and manner belonging to *cantabile* playing. The fingering 2-3, 2-3, 2-3, etc., will ensure the true phrasing of bar 23, provided a false accent on the first note of each pair be avoided.

29.—After 4 bars of manœuvring in bold chromatic steps the main theme plunges downward through an arpeggio on the dominant of G minor (bar 33), to continue during 13 bars a further evolution.

Peculiar richness and variety of tone-colouring are here created by the continuous oscillation of the figure in the middle registers of the keyboard, while larger or smaller fragments of the theme are boldly thrown, alternately, to each extreme. At bar 41 the emotional crisis sensibly approaches; the agitated figure is continuously repeated; the tempo gradually quickens and the tone becomes warmer, until the culminating chord is gained at bar 46, where it breaks into an arpeggio which sweeps through a descent of 4 octaves only to be flung upward again unrestingly.   A. R.

FANTASIA
in C minor

(Köchel No. 396.)

W. A. MOZART

Copyright 1929 by The Associated Board of the Royal Schools of Music

A. B. 284

MOZART

Fantasia in C minor
(K.396)

OPUS II

Revised and edited by York Bowen

Analytical notes by Aubyn Raymar

THE ASSOCIATED BOARD OF
THE ROYAL SCHOOLS OF MUSIC

EDITOR'S NOTE AS TO SIGNS USED IN THE TEXT

PEDAL

THIS has been marked where vitally necessary to the effect, in view of the modern piano, or where desirable in general. To skilled performers many additional pedallings may be possible with success, especially in the slower movements. The sign " P " without any following line indicates the depression and holding of pedal until the next sign " P "—*i.e.*, " legato " pedalling. In all other cases the exact duration of the pedal is clearly marked by a dotted line turned up at the end, thus: P.........⋏

PHRASING

Phrase length and construction is indicated by the use of the curved line ⁀‾‾‾‾‾‾‾‾⁀, but this does not necessarily mean " legato " as well. Dots or dashes are used to show staccato or staccatissimo, and the sign ⁑ is used for a particularly sympathetic " mezzo-staccato."

Certain important ornamental *sub-phrasings* will be found indicated at times, such as:

This indicates the delicate details of treatment, whilst the rhythmical phrase line is also shown.

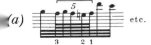 *(a)* etc.

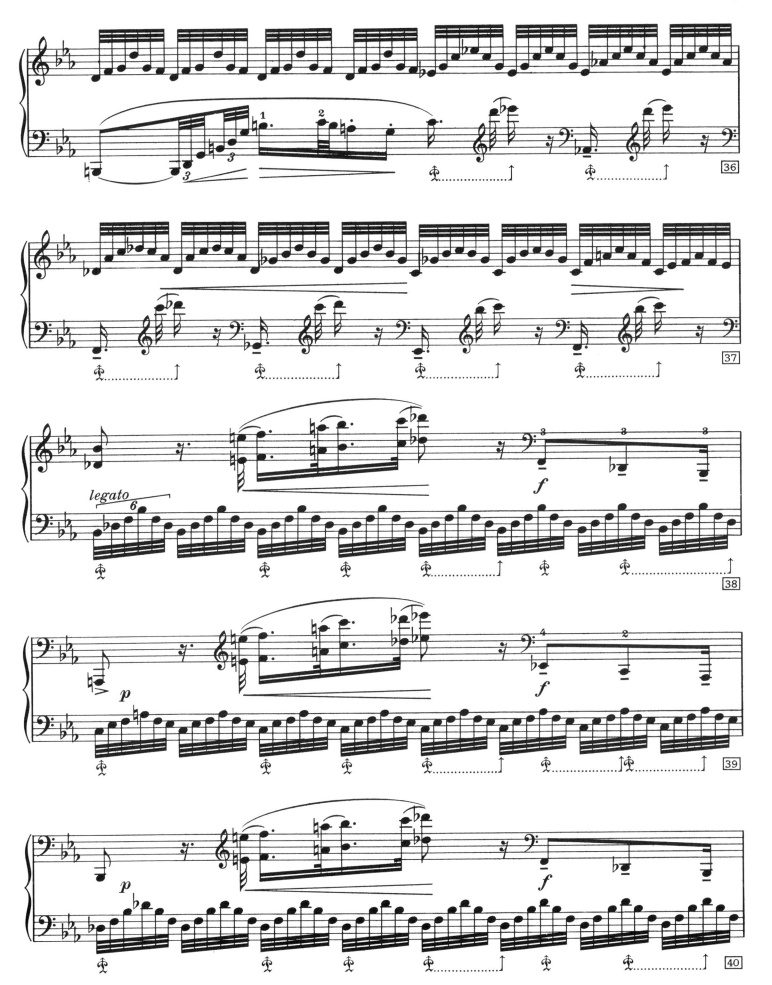

un poco agitato e pochiss accellerando

Tempo I

Printed in England by Caligraving Limited

**The Associated Board of
the Royal Schools of Music
(Publishing) Limited**

14 Bedford Square
London WC1B 3JG

ISBN 1-85472-041-4